The Riddle King's
BOOK OF JOKES, RIDDLES AND ACTIVITIES

BY
Mike Thaler

MODERN PUBLISHING
A Division of Unisystems, Inc.
New York, N.Y. 10022

Printed in Canada

Hi, Kids!

I have packed this book with
silly joke and riddle activities that
will make you laugh.

HAVE FUN!!!

Mike Thaler
The Riddle King

1

MIRROR RIDDLES

Hold this page up to a mirror to find
the riddle answer.

What fish is a real cut up?

A SWORDFISH

2

MONSTER MERRIMENT

Where do ghouls go after junior high?

Highs Ghoul

3

SILLY MULTIPLE CHOICES

Circle your FAVORITE answer and then draw it
as silly as can be in the space provided.

☞ What do caterpillars do inside cocoons?

A. Change into butterflies   C. Play tackle football
B. Play gin rummy   D. Eat pepperoni pizza

4

MIRROR RIDDLES

Hold this page up to a mirror to find
the riddle answer.

What kind of can
carries water?

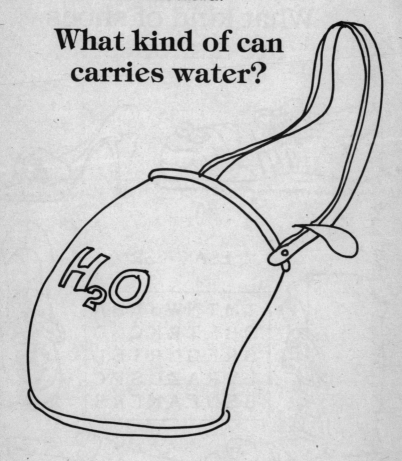

CANTEEN

5

Unscramble the riddle answer, then find it in the letter grid.
Look across, up, down, and diagonally, and circle the answer.

What kind of shoes
are dishonest?

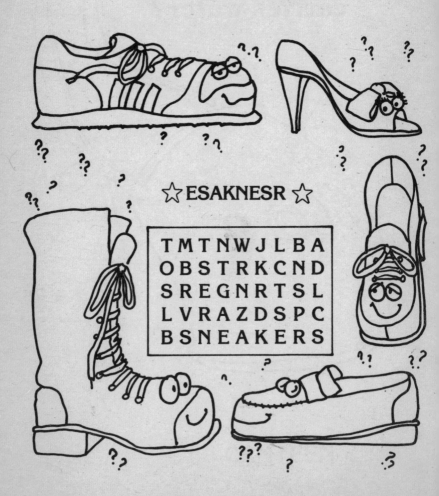

☆ ESAKNESR ☆

```
T M T N W J L B A
O B S T R K C N D
S R E G N R T S L
L V R A Z D S P C
B S N E A K E R S
```

HINK PINK SCRAMBLES

HINK PINKS are riddles that have two-word answers,
and the two words in the answer rhyme. Unscramble each word
to find the Hink Pink riddle answer.

Who rides on
a golden broom?

A   CIHR   TWCIH

_____   _____

7

WHAT IS IT??

Look at the picture. WHAT IS IT??
The letters for the answer are in the right order,
but the spacing has been changed.

AMA NCRA CKI NGASM ILE

ANSWER: _____

8

KNOCK-KNOCKS

"Knock-Knock."
"Who's there?"

"Yamaha."
"Yamaha Who?"

"Yamaha wants you to go home."

CROSSWORD RIDDLES

WORD LIST:

SORCERORITY
WITCHITA
WITCHHIKE

WITCHCONSIN
WITCHDRAWAL
WITCHER
WITCHKEY

ACROSS:

1. What is a witch's favorite American city?
4. How does a witch get free rides?
5. Where do witches like to vacation in the summer?

DOWN:

1. What does a woman trying to stop practicing witchcraft go through?
2. What do you call the witch who pitches at a witch baseball game?
3. What do you call a club for witches at college?
4. What do grown-up witches like to drink at parties?

"HAVE YOU EVER SEEN" RIDDLES

HAVE YOU EVER SEEN...

Use the code key to find the riddle answer.

△ ■ ◇ ▲ ⊟ △ ⊕ 8 ♀ ?

_ _ _ _ _ _ _ _ _ ?

A B C D E F G H I J K L M N O P Q R S T U V W X Y Z

MIRROR RIDDLES

Hold this page up to a mirror to find
the riddle answer.

What is a fish's
favorite country?

FINLAND

Unscramble the riddle answer, then find it in the letter grid.
Look across, up, down, and diagonally, and circle the answer.

What kind of pickle grows south of the Equator?

☆ TPORICLKE ☆

```
O C O F O E
L I E U G L
A S T C N K
T E H R I C
T S T L O I
R J F H U P
D G E O M O
E K M W F R
L S V A L T
```

13

Here's a Magic Letter Riddle for you —
Add or subtract letters from the underlined word to find the answer to the riddle.

When can't you open a CLOCK?

_____

WHAT IS IT??

Look at the picture. WHAT IS IT??
The letters for the answer are in the right order,
but the spacing has been changed.

ALEO PARD CHA NGINGHI SSPOTS

ANSWER: _____

15

MONSTER MAZES

This explorer wants to find a mummy.
Help him find his way.

SILLY MULTIPLE CHOICES

Circle your FAVORITE answer and then draw it
as silly as can be in the space provided.

☞ **The Pyramids in Egypt were built for —**

A. Racquetball courts

B. Tombs for Kings

C. Royal ant farms

D. Imitation volcanoes

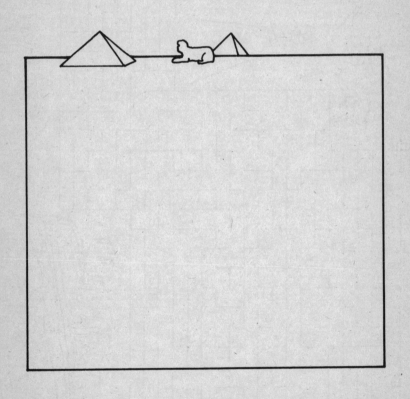

REBUS RIDDLES

Solve the rebus puzzle below to find the
riddle answer. First spell the object, then
subtract and add letters as instructed.

What can is a monster?

FR + [tank] − T [can] [stairs] − P + [nail] − P

___ ___ ___ - ___ ___ ___ - ___ ___ ___ ___

CROSSWORD RIDDLES

WORD LIST:

AIRPORK
BIHOGRAPHY
HAMERICA
HAMBRELLA

HAMPHIBIAN
HAMBASSADOR
HAMPER
OINKMENT

PIGNIC
PORKESTRA
SMELLAVISION

ACROSS:

4. What country has the most free pigs?
7. What do you call a pig who keeps you dry when it is raining?
8. What do you call it when a group of pigs take a basket of food out in the country?
9. What do you call a group of pigs playing musical instruments together?
10. Where do pigs land their planes?
11. What do you get if you cross a frog with a pig?

DOWN:

1. What do you call a book about a pig's life?
2. What do you give a pig when it scrapes its knee?
3. What do you call a pig who is a diplomatic official?
5. What do pigs like to watch at night?
6. Where do you put dirty pigs?

HINK PINK SCRAMBLES

HINK PINKS are riddles that have two-word answers,
and the two words in the answer rhyme. Unscramble each word
to find the Hink Pink riddle answer.

What do you call a croaker who fell off his lilypad?

A   GOYSG   GROGFY

_____   _____

Here's a Magic Letter Riddle for you —

Add or subtract letters from the underlined word to find the answer to the riddle.

When is a <u>CAR</u> sent on someone's birthday?

_____

SILLY MULTIPLE CHOICES

Circle your FAVORITE answer and then draw it
as silly as can be in the space provided.

☞ # A camel's hump is filled with —
A. Water   C. Baby camels
B. Chocolate milk   D. Spare change

22

WHO IS THIS?

Choose the right answer and write it on the line below.

What pickle pecks on wood and is a famous cartoon character?

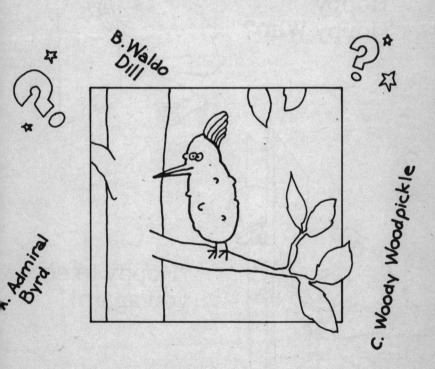

B. Waldo Dill

C. Woody Woodpickle

A. Admiral Byrd

_____

23

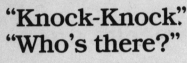

"Knock-Knock."
"Who's there?"

"Hoppy."
"Hoppy Who?"

"Hoppy to see you again!"

Unscramble the riddle answer, then find it in the letter grid.
Look across, up, down, and diagonally, and circle the answer.

What do you call a person who stuffs cabs?

☆ TXAIREDMSTI ☆

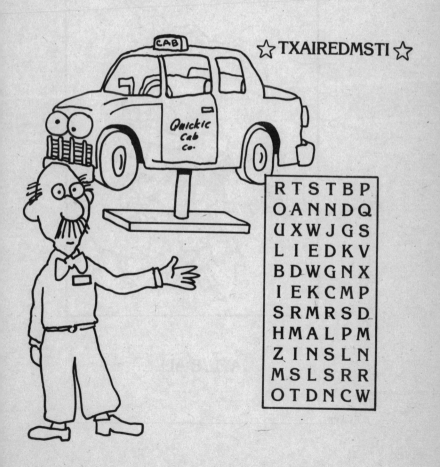

```
R T S T B P
O A N N D Q
U X W J G S
L I E D K V
B D W G N X
I E K C M P
S R M R S D
H M A L P M
Z I N S L N
M S L S R R
O T D N C W
```

25

WHAT IS IT??

Look at the picture. WHAT IS IT??
The letters for the answer are in the right order,
but the spacing has been changed.

AFLYB ALL

ANSWER: _____

"HAVE YOU EVER SEEN" RIDDLES

HAVE YOU EVER SEEN...

Use the code key to find the riddle answer.

△ ⚡   ⚌ △ ▲▲▲ ◇ ⊟ ?

— —   — — — — — — ?

A B C D E F G H I J K L M N O P Q R S T U V W X Y Z

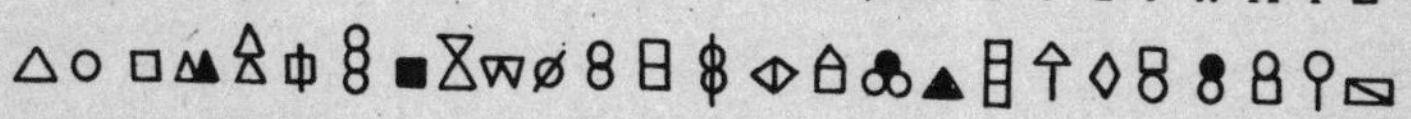

△ ○ ▢ ▲ ⚌ ⚭ 8 ▪ ⊠ �w ⊘ 8 ⊟ ⚡ ◇ ⬠ ⚭ ▲ ▮ ⊟ ⇧ ◇ 8 8 ⚲ ▱

CROSSWORD RIDDLES

WORD LIST:

ALLIGARTERS   RUBBERBANDIT   TOOTHPICKLE
MERRYTHON   SERFING   TURBANTINE
OLIVEPHANT   TENNIS   TWOSDAY

ACROSS:

3. What is green and sour and cleans your teeth?
5. What's green, weighs 2,000 pounds and can float in a martini?
6. What is the happiest Olympic event?
7. What do you call a person who steals rubberbands?
8. What was a favorite sport during the Middle Ages?

DOWN:

1. What's green, has a lot of teeth and holds up your socks?
2. What number is a game?
3. What day has its own number?
4. How does a sultan clean his turban?

28

WHO IS THIS?

Choose the right answer and write it on the line below.

What frog was a famous Indian Chief?

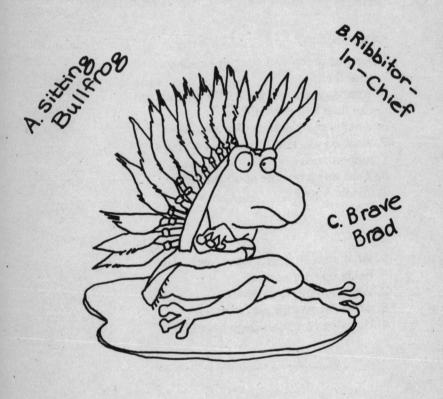

A. Sitting Bullfrog

B. Ribbitor-In-Chief

C. Brave Brad

_____

Here's a Magic Letter Riddle for you —

Add or subtract letters from the underlined word to find the answer to the riddle.

How can <u>AIR</u> be curly?

_____

REBUS RIDDLES

Solve the rebus puzzle below to find the
riddle answer. First spell the object, then
subtract and add letters as instructed.

What kind of can flies over the ocean and eats a lot of fish?

___ ___ ___ ___ ___ ___ ___

31

WHAT IS IT??

Look at the picture. WHAT IS IT??
The letters for the answer are in the right order,
but the spacing has been changed.

ARE PORT ERWI THTWOS COOPS

ANSWER: _____

REBUS RIDDLES

Solve the rebus puzzle below to find the
riddle answer. First spell the object, then
subtract and add letters as instructed.

What is the smartest
kind of bean?

— ————— ————

"HAVE YOU EVER SEEN" RIDDLES

HAVE YOU EVER SEEN...

Use the code key to find the riddle answer.

△ ○◆⊟✕$⊟ ⊟△↑□■?

_ _____ _____?

A	B	C	D	E	F	G	H	I	J	K	L	M	N	O	P	Q	R	S	T	U	V	W	X	Y	Z
△	○	□	▲	△	⏀	⏀	8	■	✕	⍵	⌀	8	⊟	$	◆	⌂	♣	▲	⊟	↑	◇	8	8	�	▱

34

CROSSWORD RIDDLES

WORD LIST:

CONDUCKTOR   DUCKSHUND   FIREQUACKER
DUCKTIONARY   DUCKSYLAND   QUACK
DUCKATESSEN   DUCKTAPHONE   QUACKUP
DUCKEDO   EDUCKADTED   QUAKER
DUCKTATOR

ACROSS:

3. What book does a duck use to find the meaning of a word?
4. What do you call a duck doctor?
5. Where do ducks go to eat corned beef on rye?
7. What do you call it when a duck crashes?
9. What does a duck wear when he dresses up?
12. What do you call a duck that leads an orchestra?
13. What religion are most ducks?

DOWN:

1. What do you call a smart duck who has spent lots of time in school?
2. What do you call an explosive duck?
6. What do you get if you cross a duck and a potato?
8. What kind of pet looks like a hot dog and quacks?
10. What kind of music do jazzy ducks play?
11. What machine does every duck secretary use?

35

WHAT IS IT??

Look at the picture. WHAT IS IT??
The letters for the answer are in the right order,
but the spacing has been changed.

ALA DYPUR SING HERLIP S

ANSWER: _____

WHO IS THIS?

Choose the right answer and write it on the line below.

What toad helped the Lone Ranger?

_____

Unscramble the riddle answer, then find it in the letter grid.
Look across, up, down, and diagonally, and circle the answer.

What make of car is hardest to hit?

☆ DGDOE ☆

```
S N O N E
C H N G O
K L D P R
R O M N I
D N U B A
```

KNOCK-KNOCKS

"Knock-Knock."
"Who's there?"

"Aurora."
"Aurora Who?"

"Aurora means there's a lion at the door."

39

MIRROR RIDDLES

Hold this page up to a mirror to find
the riddle answer.

What state do
cows like best?

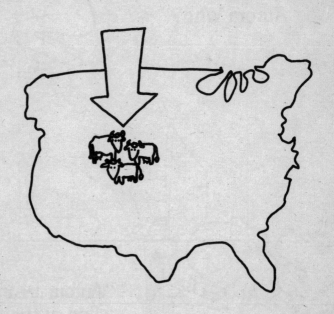

COWLORADO

40

WHAT IS IT??

Look at the picture. WHAT IS IT??
The letters for the answer are in the right order,
but the spacing has been changed.

AR USSI AND RESSI NGONT OPOFAS ALAD

ANSWER: _____

41

CROSSWORD RIDDLES

WORD LIST:

AUTOBIOGRAPHY   MAROON   STAMPEDE
CZARDINE   NAPKINS   TOADSTOOL
EXPRESSO   PEARADE   WASHINGTON
HOLESALE

ACROSS:

1. What do you call the King of Russian Sardines?
8. What is it called when an automobile writes a book about itself?
9. What color do people turn when they are left on desert islands?
10. What's the cheapest way to buy holes?

DOWN:

2. What always sleeps through dinner?
3. What's the fastest coffee in the world?
4. What president did the most laundry?
5. What's the most difficult stool to sit on?
6. What's it called when three pears walk down the street?
7. What's it called when a lot of stamps run out of the post office?

42

SILLY MULTIPLE CHOICES

Circle your FAVORITE answer and then draw it
as silly as can be in the space provided.

After the sun sets, it —
A. Goes to Florida
B. Shines on the other
side of the Earth
C. Goes to bed
D. Goes out dancing

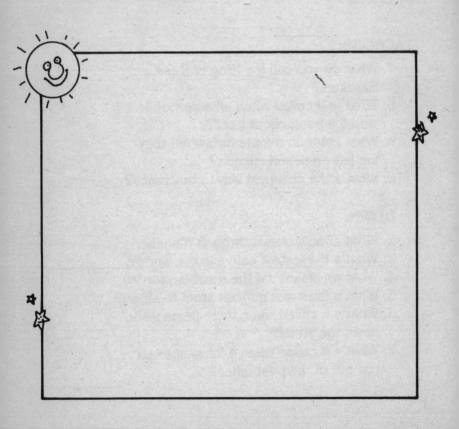

CARTOON RIDDLES

Here are three
MIXED-UP MACHINES

——————— Can you draw one? ———————

MONSTER MAZES

**Can you help this witch find
her lost friend, Frank?**

MIRROR RIDDLES

Hold this page up to a mirror to find
the riddle answer.

What sweet food
do cans love?

CANDY

Unscramble the riddle answer, then find it in the letter grid.
Look across, up, down, and diagonally, and circle the answer.

What do you call a person who steals walruses?

☆ AWLRSUTLER ☆

```
W O M Q V M Z X W T
N A F H J K M O P S
A G L D C A R E V E
V R N R M U E L S T
L Y E N U A S R E H
Y S P Y S S S T O P
S M H N V L T R I C
T L O I A E B L H B
V S R A P T A A E I
I T V L H S P U O R
```

REBUS RIDDLES

Solve the rebus puzzle below to find the riddle answer. First spell the object, then subtract and add letters as instructed.

What do you call mice that grow on the floor of caves?

—— —— —— —— —— —— —— —— —— ——

HINK PINK SCRAMBLES

HINK PINKS are riddles that have two-word answers,
and the two words in the answer rhyme. Unscramble each word
to find the Hink Pink riddle answer.

What do you call an old sea mammal?

A   ALSET   HWLEA

_____ _____

49

WHAT IS IT??

Look at the picture. WHAT IS IT??
The letters for the answer are in the right order,
but the spacing has been changed.

AMANW RENC HINGH ISN ECK

ANSWER: _____

"HAVE YOU EVER SEEN" RIDDLES

HAVE YOU EVER SEEN...

Use the code key to find the riddle answer.

⇧⧗⊟⧖ φ8የ ?

____ ___ ?

A	B	C	D	E	F	G	H	I	J	K	L	M	N	O	P	Q	R	S	T	U	V	W	X	Y	Z
△	○	□	▲	⧖	φ	8	■	⧗	ѡ	ø	8	⊟	⧖	◇	⬠	♣	▲	⊟	⇧	◇	8	8	⧖	የ	⬚

MONSTER MAZES

**This ghost wants an ice scream soda.
Can you help him?**

CARTOON RIDDLES

Here are three
ADVANTAGES OF BEING
CERTAIN ANIMALS

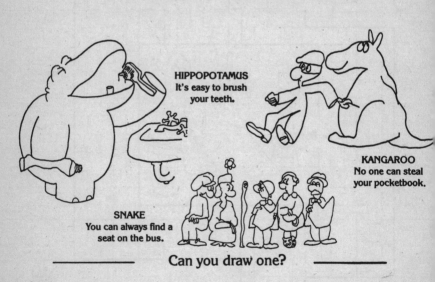

HIPPOPOTAMUS
It's easy to brush
your teeth.

KANGAROO
No one can steal
your pocketbook.

SNAKE
You can always find a
seat on the bus.

Can you draw one?

ANSWERS

```
T M T N W J L B A
O B S T R K C N D
S R E G N R T S L
L V R A Z D S P C
B S N E A K E R S
```

A Rich Witch

A Man Cracking A Smile

0 A Horsefly

2
```
O C O F O E
L I E U G L
A S T C N K
T E H R I C
T S T L O I
R J F H U P
D G E O M O
E K M W F R
L S V A L T
```

13 When you take away the C and it becomes a LOCK.

14 A Leopard Changing His Spots

15

17 Frank-can-stein

18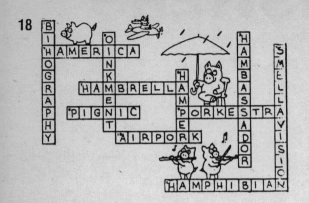

19 A Soggy Froggy

20 When you add a D to make it a CARD.

22 C. Woody Woodpickle

24
```
R T S T B P
O A N N D Q
U X W J G S
L I E D K V
B D W G N X
I E K C M P
S R M R S D
H M A L P M
Z I N S L N
M S L S R R
O T D N C W
```

25 A Fly Ball

26 An Eardrum

27 (crossword: TOOTHPICKLE · WOSDAY · URBANTINE · ALLIGATTER · OLIVEPHANT · TENNIS · MERRYTHON · RUBBERBANDIT · SERFING)

28 A Sitting Bullfrog

29 When you add an H and it becomes HAIR.

30 Pelican

31 A Reporter with Two Scoops

32 A Human Bean

3 A Boxing Match

44

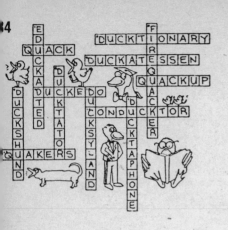

Crossword grid answers:
- EDUCATED
- QUACK
- DUCKTIONARY
- FIREQUACKER
- DUCKATESSEN
- QUACKUP
- DUCKSHUND
- DUCKTATOR
- DUCKE
- DUCKSYLAND
- CONDUCKTOR
- QUAKERS
- DUCKTAPHONE

5 A Lady Pursing Her Lips

6 B. Tontoad

44

7

```
S N O N E
C H N G O
K L D P R
R O M N I
D N U B A
```

0 A Russian Dressing on
   Top of a Salad

1

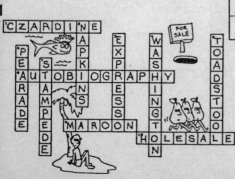

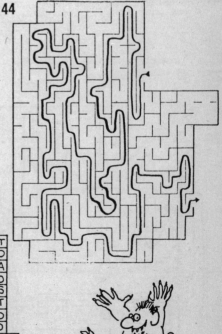

Crossword grid answers:
- CZARDINE
- NAPKINS
- EXPRESS
- WASHINGTON
- TOADSTOOL
- PERADE
- STAMPEDE
- AUTOBIOGRAPHY
- MAROON
- HOLESALE

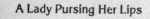

46

```
W O M Q V M Z X W T
N A F H J K M O P S
A G L D C A R E V E
V R N R M U E L S T
L Y E N U A S R E H
Y S P Y S S S T O P
S M H N V L T R I C
T L O I A E B L H B
V S R A P T A A E I
I T V L H S P U C R
```

47 Stalagmice

48 A Stale Whale

49 A Man Wrenching His Neck

50 Time Fly

51

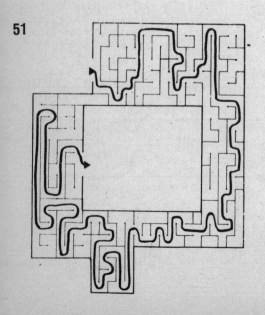